MAKE ME LAUGH!

CONTENTS

A LAUGHING

What do you do when
someone tells you
not to laugh?
Do you stop laughing?
Or do you laugh
even more?

When you start
to laugh, it can
be hard to stop.
Your body shakes.
You try to hold
your breath.
Sometimes just the
sound of laughing
makes you laugh
even more.

"Don't laugh!"

"Shhhhhhh!"

Did You Know?
Kids laugh more than
grown-ups.

MATTER

Written by Laura Hirschfield

Why is it hard to stop laughing?
No one really knows.
But many people think
it's just because it feels
so good to laugh!

Did You Know?

The top four most ticklish spots are the feet, the armpits, the neck, and under the chin.

"It's not funny!"

"Be quiet!"

Laughing feels good.
But did you know
laughing is good for you, too?
If you are sick, or hurt,
laughing can help you get better.
It can help you relax.
It can help you forget what hurts.

Did You Know?
Chimps and gorillas laugh
when they're tickled.

Some scientists
say girls laugh more
than boys. What do
you think?

4

What Happens When You Laugh

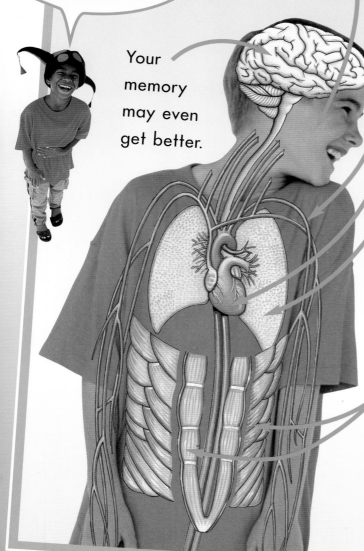

What else happens to your body when you laugh?

Your memory may even get better.

Fifteen muscles in your face move.

Chemicals that help you fight sickness and stress flow through your body.

Your heart beats faster.

More air goes into your lungs. (This can help people who have a hard time breathing.)

Your stomach muscles tighten and then relax. (This can help pain in your body go away.)

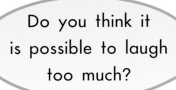

Do you think it is possible to laugh too much?

Doctors know that
laughing is good for you.
Some hospitals have parties
and games for sick children.
They ask famous people to visit the kids.
They have clowns and magic shows.
They have jugglers
and puppet shows.

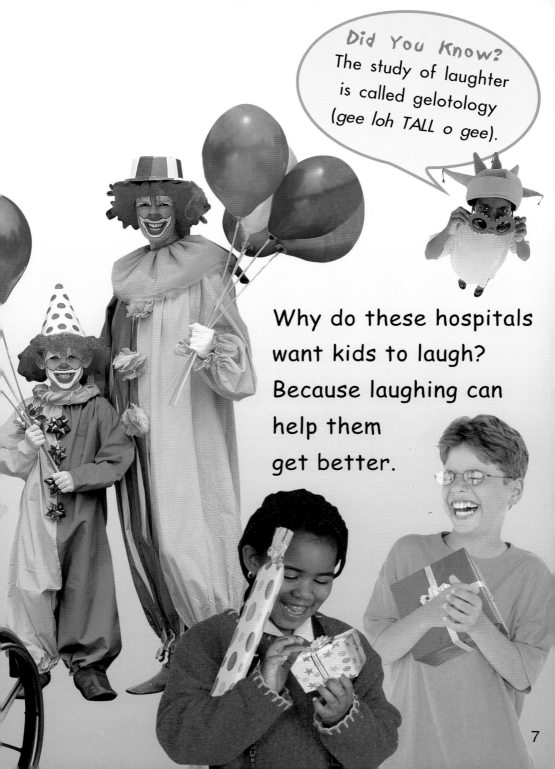

Why do these hospitals want kids to laugh? Because laughing can help them get better.

7

The Girl Who Wouldn't Laugh

Written by Milo & Mason
Illustrated by Sandra Cammell

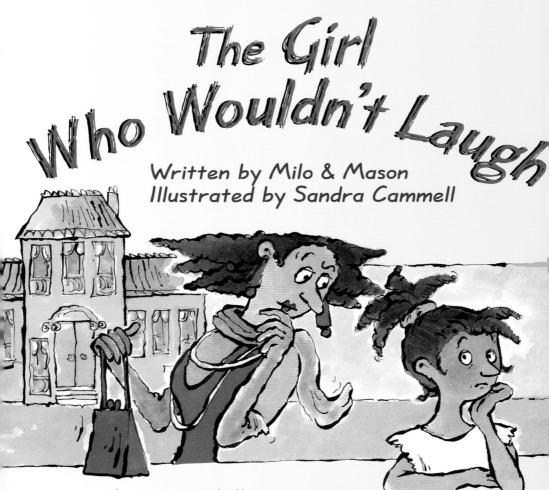

Once there was a billionaire.

(A billionaire is a really, really, REALLY rich person.)

She lived with her daughter, Wanda, in a mansion.

(A mansion is a really, really, REALLY fancy house.)

The billionaire was upset.

Wanda had never laughed in her whole life.

Not once! So the billionaire offered a prize.

The first person to make Wanda laugh
would win a big bag of money!

A long line formed outside the mansion.
There were comedians and clowns and jesters.
They told Wanda jokes.
They made funny faces.
They slipped on banana peels.
But did anything work?
No! Wanda didn't even smile!
She thought they were
boring, boring, BORING!

Wanda looked out
the window and sighed.
She saw a boy named Jack.
He was walking home from the store.
His mother had sent him to buy apples.
Jack dragged the bag of apples behind him.
The bag got a hole in it.
The apples fell out one by one.
Jack didn't even see them.

Why do you think
Jack hasn't noticed he's
losing the apples?

"Hey, Jack!" Wanda cried.
"Hold the bag up!
Don't let it drag on the ground!"

"What a good idea!" said Jack. "Thanks!"

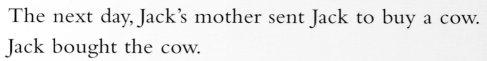

The next day, Jack's mother sent Jack to buy a cow.
Jack bought the cow.
Then he remembered what Wanda had said.
So he carried the cow home.
It was really, really, REALLY heavy!

Jack walked by the mansion.
Wanda saw him.

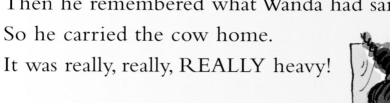

"Hey, Jack!" she shouted.
"You're not supposed to carry a cow!
Ride it instead! That would be easier!"

"What a good idea!" said Jack. "Thanks!"

The next day, Jack's mother sent Jack
to the store again.
She wanted a watermelon.
Jack remembered what Wanda had said.
He sat on the watermelon.
He told the watermelon, "Giddyap!"
He rode the watermelon home.

Jack rode by the mansion.

Wanda saw Jack.

He looked really, really, REALLY silly.

She burst out laughing.

The billionaire heard Wanda laugh.
"You win the prize!" she told Jack.
She gave Jack a big bag of money.

"Thanks!" said Jack.

Jack was happy.

He took the money home.

But what do you think that silly boy did?

He dragged the bag behind him.

The bag got a hole in it.

The money fell out bit by bit.

And Jack didn't even see it.

How do you think Jack will feel when he gets home?

LAUGH AT ME

Interview by Sharon Griggins

Nancy Gibson is a comedian. She is on a TV comedy show. She also helps write comedy for the show.

A I was in the seventh grade. We had a school talent show. I did some funny skits with my friends. I felt so good when people laughed.

Comedy groups write and perform skits on TV or on stage.

19

Q How do you get your ideas?

A I get most of my ideas from things that happen to me.

For example, one day
I went to the shoe store.
The salesman was clumsy.
He dropped ten boxes of shoes
all over the floor.
I might make up a joke about that.
But I would add more funny parts
to the story.

What funny parts would you add to Nancy's shoe story?

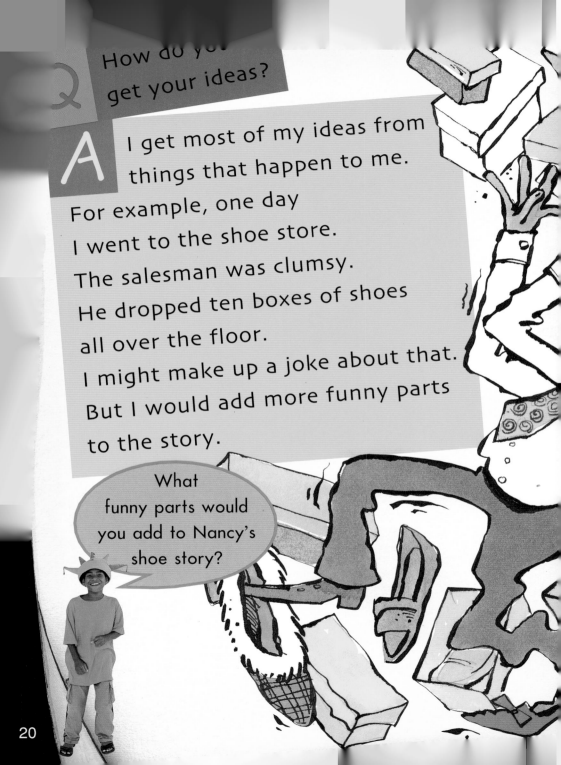

How can you become a comedian?

A Good comedians see the funny things in life. Look for things that seem funny. Write them down. Tell them to your friends. And see if you can get a laugh!

Comedians use their faces and bodies when they tell a funny story.

Q Do you have to be funny to be a comedian?

A Everyone is funny. But some people are funnier than others. Can you stand up in front of a big group? Can you make all the people laugh? Then you can be a good comedian!

Just Jokes

Written by Chuck L. Mann
Illustrated by Fraser Williamson

Animal Antics

What's green
and loud?

A froghorn!

How do you
catch a fish?

Have someone
throw it to you!

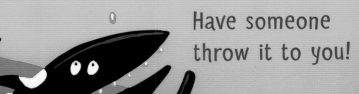

What do hippos have
that no other animal has?

Baby hippos!

What happens
if a snake bites you?

You're hiss-tory.

Why do lions
eat raw meat?

They can't cook.

Where should you never take a dog shopping?

A flea market.

What do you call a fly with no wings?

A walk.

How do you get an elephant in the refrigerator?

Open the door and put it in.

How do you get an alligator in the refrigerator?

Open the door, take out the elephant, and put in the alligator.

Joke Telling
Dos and Don'ts

Don't forget the punch line.

Don't laugh before you tell the joke.

Don't laugh before you finish the joke.

Do laugh after you tell the joke.

Ride the Cool Bus

How do rock stars get to school?

On a cool bus.

How do lifeguards get to school?

On a pool bus.

How do bullies get to school?

On a cruel bus.

How do bees get to school?

On a school buzz.

How do athletes get to school?

They race.

Make Your Own Joke

There are many kinds of jokes.
A joke can be a kind of wordplay.
A joke can be a kind of surprise.
Here is one way to make up a joke.

Think of a famous place or name.

New York City

Change it a little bit.
This will be
the punch line.

New Pork City

Think of a question
that suggests your punch line.

> Where do pigs go
> for a night on the town?

Put it all together.

> Where do pigs go
> for a night on the town?
> New Pork City!

Index